Alex
CALLS THE SHOTS

CHARLES PEATTIE
AND
RUSSELL TAYLOR

HEADLINE

First published in 1993
by HEADLINE BOOK PUBLISHING PLC

10 9 8 7 6 5 4 3 2 1

ISBN 0 7472 7872 5

Printed and bound in Great Britain by
BPCC Hazell Books Ltd
Member of BPCC Ltd

HEADLINE BOOK PUBLISHING PLC
Headline House
79 Great Titchfield Street
London W1P 7FN

Alex   Wendy (his secretary)

Alex's wife Penny.   Their son : Christopher.

Clive + his girlfriend Bridget.

Greg. Alex's brother ; A journalist.

Ruth + Clio.

Rupert
(Alex's boss)

Alex PEATTIE + TAYLOR

THANK YOU FOR THE PRESENTATION. I THINK I CAN SAFELY SAY THAT MY COMPANY IS MOST INTERESTED IN TAKING PREMISES OUT HERE IN DOCKLANDS.

REALLY?

DOCKLAND

YES. YOU SEE MOST OF OUR CLIENTS ARE DRAWN FROM THE RANKS OF THE LARGER MERCHANT BANKS AND STOCKBROKING HOUSES. BEING BASED HERE WILL GREATLY FACILITATE OUR DEALINGS WITH THEM.

THAT'S WONDERFUL.

I'M PARTICULARLY IMPRESSED BY THE NUMBER OF SUCH FINANCIAL INSTITUTIONS YOU'VE MANAGED TO GET TO MOVE OUT HERE...

YOU ARE...?

YES. PRACTICALLY NONE... ALL IN ALL A MOST DISCREET LOCATION FOR US.

OH... YOU'RE HEADHUNTERS.

Alex PEATTIE + TAYLOR

I'M SORRY MARTIN...I'M A BIT NEW TO CITY JOURNALISM.

YOUR CONDUCT MADE US BOTH LOOK TOTAL FOOLS IN THAT PRIVATE BRIEFING WITH ALEX MASTERLEY.

LOOK: AS REGARDS ARRANGEMENTS BETWEEN THE PRESS AND THE CITY THERE ARE SUCH THINGS AS MEETINGS WHICH SHOULD BE UNDERSTOOD BY BOTH PARTIES AS TO BE NEVER TAKING PLACE...

OH DEAR. ME ATTEMPTING TO PLACE SOMETHING ON RECORD. WHAT A GAFFE.

...AND YOU MUST REALISE THAT AS FAR AS EITHER SIDE IS CONCERNED ANY KNOWLEDGE OF THESE MEETINGS WILL BE DENIED IF THEY'RE EVER ENQUIRED ABOUT LATER.

YES. I SEE... I'M REALLY SORRY.

OKAY SO NEXT TIME DON'T EMBARRASS ME BY TAKING OUT YOUR DIARY WHEN HE SAYS "WE MUST HAVE LUNCH SOMETIME".

I THOUGHT HE MEANT IT.

Alex PEATTIE + TAYLOR

BUT MEGABANK IS PAYING US A LOT OF MONEY FOR THIS TIME AND MOTION STUDY OF THEIR CORPORATE FINANCE DEPARTMENT.

I KNOW...

BUT I FEEL DREADFUL ABOUT PRESENTING OUR RECOMMENDATIONS. AFTER ALL, I'M NOT JUST A MANAGEMENT CONSULTANT... I'M A HUMAN BEING AS WELL.

HOW CAN ONE CARE ABOUT THE STRICT APPLICATION OF ABSTRACT PRINCIPLES OF BUSINESS MANAGEMENT WHEN PEOPLE'S JOBS ARE AT STAKE HERE?

I MEAN SURELY WE CAN DO SOMETHING TO MAKE OUR FINDINGS A LITTLE LESS EXTREME?

HMMM...

YOU MEAN CLAIM THE DEPARTMENT IS RATHER INEFFICIENT AND RECOMMEND SOME CUTBACKS?

WELL, THEY WON'T BOTHER TO EMPLOY US AGAIN IF WE SAY EVERYTHING'S FINE.

Alex — PEATTIE + TAYLOR

Panel 1: SO ALEX ISN'T TOO BADLY INJURED? / NO. BUT HE'LL HAVE TO WEAR A NECKBRACE... AND HIS WRISTS ARE BADLY SPRAINED...

Panel 2: OF COURSE HE'S ANXIOUS TO GET BACK TO HIS DESK AS SOON AS HE'S DISCHARGED FROM HOSPITAL. / THIS IS ONE OF THE SITUATIONS I DREAD...

Panel 3: THESE STUPID STUBBORN PEOPLE WHO INSIST ON BEING DIFFERENT FROM EVERYONE ELSE AND PUSH THEMSELVES TO PERFORM TASKS WHICH ARE BEYOND THEIR CAPABILITIES...

Panel 4: IT'S AGONISING TO OBSERVE THEIR SLOW TORTUOUS PROGRESS AS THEY TAKE HOURS JUST TO WRITE A SIMPLE SENTENCE. / I KNOW WHAT YOU MEAN...

Panel 5: JUST PUT "GET WELL SOON, LOVE CLIVE." THERE ARE 14 OTHER PEOPLE TO SIGN THAT CARD. / I'M TRYING TO THINK OF SOMETHING WITTY.

Alex — PEATTIE + TAYLOR

Panel 1: GOOD GRIEF, ALEX... YOU LOOK A FRIGHT. / ER... YES... ABOUT MY ACCIDENT, CLIVE...

Panel 2: I'M TELLING EVERYONE HERE AT THE BANK THAT I HAD A FALL FROM A HORSE. I'D APPRECIATE IT IF YOU'D KEEP MUM ABOUT WHAT REALLY HAPPENED. / YOU CAN COUNT ON ME.

Panel 3: THANKS, CLIVE. I WOULDN'T WANT WORD TO GET ROUND THAT MY WIFE DELIBERATELY ATTEMPTED TO RUN ME DOWN IN THE CAR... / I QUITE UNDERSTAND.

Panel 4: UNDER THE BANK'S LEASING SCHEME YOU'D BE LIABLE TO PAY A PERCENTAGE OF THE DAMAGE INSURANCE CLAIM. / I'LL JUST SAY IT WAS LEFT PARKED OVERNIGHT AND ANOTHER VEHICLE MUST HAVE BUMPED INTO IT.

Alex
PEATTIE + TAYLOR

moulin et
RESTAURANT FRA

YOU DIDN'T USED TO COME HERE WITH "THAT WOMAN" DID YOU, ALEX?

I'M AFRAID SO, PENNY.

MENU

WENDY AND I USED TO SECLUDE OURSELVES AT A DIMLY-LIT TABLE OVER THERE IN THE CORNER FOR FURTIVE SUPPERS. IN THE END IT CONTRIBUTED TO OUR BREAK-UP, I SUPPOSE...

I JUST FOUND IT SO UNBEARABLE THE WAY SOCIETY'S MORAL APPROBATION FORCED ME TO HIDE MY RELATIONSHIP WITH A VERY SPECIAL PERSON.

WHAT?

OH... THE MAITRE D'...

AH... GOOD EVENING, MR MASTERLEY. YOUR USUAL TABLE?

CERTAINLY NOT, MARCEL. GIVE US A CENTRAL ONE RIGHT BY THE WINDOW, S'IL VOUS PLAIT.

Alex
PEATTIE + TAYLOR

HMM... SO THIS IS THE RUFFIAN WE'RE DEALING WITH?

...RIGHT... IF YOU EVER WANT TO SEE ALEX MASTERLEY ALIVE... LISTEN TO ME...

I WANT £100,000 IN USED £10 NOTES IN A GREEN CANVAS HOLD-ALL...

£100,000... ...USED TENNERS.

HOLD ON, GENTLEMEN. WE'RE ALL ANXIOUS FOR ALEX'S SAFE RETURN BUT ARE WE ALLOWING OURSELVES TO BE COMPROMISED HERE?

CLICK

WE ARE SENIOR BOARD MEMBERS OF MEGABANK. SHOULD WE REALLY BE ALLOWING SOME CRIMINAL TO DICTATE TERMS TO US?

QUITE RIGHT...

I'LL GET ONE OF THE AUDIO TYPISTS TO TYPE IT UP TOMORROW AND PUT COPIES IN OUR IN-TRAYS.

MUCH MORE SEEMLY.

Alex PEATTIE + TAYLOR

...AND THE KIDNAPPER IS DEMANDING £100,000 FOR ALEX'S SAFE RETURN.

THAT'S A LOT OF MONEY, MR STERLING.

EXACTLY. NOW OBVIOUSLY WE'VE BEEN GIVEN STRICT INSTRUCTIONS NOT TO GO TO THE POLICE... THEN I THOUGHT OF YOU.

I KNOW YOUR AGENCY'S DISCRETION CAN BE RELIED UPON SO I'D LIKE YOU TO PUT OUT SOME FEELERS FOR US, SEE WHAT YOU CAN TURN UP...

OKAY...

GIVE ME A DESCRIPTION OF THE PERSON YOU'RE LOOKING FOR AND I'LL SEE WHAT I CAN DO...

RIGHT...

CORPORATE FINANCE MANAGER, EARLY 30s, WIDE EXPERIENCE OF M+A WORK, SALARY NEGOTIABLE, PLUS CAR...

FINE. MY SEARCH FEE WILL BE £35,000...

SOUNDS LIKE A BARGAIN...

DARWIN+TRENT EXECUTIVE RECRUITMENT.

Alex PEATTIE + TAYLOR

NEWS ROOM

HOW ARE YOUR PARENTS COPING WITH YOUR BROTHER ALEX'S KIDNAP, GREG?

WELL, MY FATHER WILL BE OKAY. HE'S ONE OF THOSE TYPICALLY BRITISH TACITURN, INTROVERTED, SELF-RELIANT TYPES. I'VE NO WORRIES ABOUT HIM...

IT'S A FAR MORE DIFFICULT SITUATION FOR MY MOTHER TO HANDLE THOUGH. SHE HAS A MUCH MORE OPEN EMOTIONAL TEMPERAMENT. I'M AFRAID SHE'S HAD TO BE PLACED UNDER HEAVY SEDATION.

I UNDERSTAND.

SHE'LL TALK TO ANYONE.

YOU WOULDN'T WANT ANY OTHER JOURNALISTS MUSCLING IN ON YOUR STORY.

Alex
PEATTIE + TAYLOR

GOOD GRIEF. WHAT KIND OF PEOPLE ARE YOU? HAVE YOU NEVER GIVEN ANY THOUGHT TO WHAT THE VICTIMS OF THIS HATEFUL PROCESS SUFFER?...THE LIMBO THEY HAVE TO EXIST IN?

LOOK DON'T GET HYSTERICAL...

...NEVER KNOWING WHERE THEY ARE OR WHERE IT WILL END... AND NOT BEING ABLE TO COMMUNICATE WITH ANYBODY....

SHUT UP WILL YOU?

...BEING KEPT IN THE DARK AND IN CHAINS...FOR MONTHS MAYBE... THE NERVERACKING WAIT TO SEE IF THE OTHER PARTY WILL COME UP WITH THE MONEY...

ALL RIGHT. YOU'VE MADE YOUR POINT.

...SO THE IDEA OF SELLING A HOUSE TO RAISE RANSOM PAYMENT IS NOT A VIABLE PROPOSITION AT THE MOMENT...

QUITE. AND THAT'S JUST THE CONVEYANCING...WE'VE NOT EVEN LOOKED AT THE PROBLEM OF FINDING A BUYER...

Alex
PEATTIE + TAYLOR

IT WAS HELL, PENNY. UNLESS YOU'D BEEN THROUGH IT YOU COULD NEVER IMAGINE WHAT IT WAS LIKE...

THE BOREDOM WAS THE WORST THING... BEING FORCED TO SIT THERE ALL DAY WITH NOTHING TO DO AND NOTHING TO LOOK FORWARD TO EXCEPT MEAL TIMES. YOU HAVE TO INVENT TASKS TO KEEP YOURSELF OCCUPIED.

AND THEN THE UNCERTAINTY, THE FEAR... WILL YOU SURVIVE? YOUR FATE IS IN THE HANDS OF OTHERS... AT ANY MOMENT THE DOOR COULD OPEN AND YOU COULD BE OUT OF THERE...

OKAY.

SO THAT WAS YOUR FIRST DAY BACK AT WORK, NOW WHAT ABOUT YOUR KIDNAP ORDEAL?

ER... PIECE OF CAKE, ACTUALLY.

Alex PEATTIE + TAYLOR

PENNY. THE JACKSONS ARE AWAY AREN'T THEY?

YES THEY'RE IN WALES FOR THE WEEKEND.

FUNNY... BACK IN THE 80s WE USED TO MOVE HOUSE SO OFTEN THAT WE NEVER REALLY KNEW OR CARED ABOUT OUR NEIGHBOURS.

THERE'S A COUPLE OF SUSPICIOUS-LOOKING TYPES GOING INTO THEIR HOUSE...

NOW WE'VE LIVED HERE A FEW YEARS THERE'S MUCH MORE OF A SENSE OF COMMUNITY IN WHICH PEOPLE SHOW A MUTUAL CONCERN ABOUT EACH OTHER'S PROPERTY

HOLD ON. IT'S O.K.... NOTHING TO BE ALARMED ABOUT...

THEY'RE RANSACKING THE PLACE... THEY'RE ONLY BURGLARS - NOT AN ESTATE AGENT AND PROSPECTIVE BUYER...

FOR SALE

FOR SALE

FOR SALE

FOR SALE

Alex PEATTIE + TAYLOR

RUTH, THIS TIME YOU'VE TAKEN OFF WORK RECENTLY... FOR THE PURPOSES OF THIS HEALTH INSURANCE POLICY I'LL NEED TO KNOW THE REASON.

ER... "FEMININE PROBLEMS"

HEY. YOU DON'T NEED TO USE THESE EUPHEMISMS WITH ME. I'M A WOMAN TOO, REMEMBER...

THAT'S WHY I'M ASSIGNED TO OUR FEMALE CLIENTS, SO THEY'LL FEEL ABLE TO TALK FREELY ABOUT THESE SENSITIVE MATTERS...

SORRY. FORCE OF HABIT... I WORK IN AN ALL-MALE OFFICE...

WHAT I MEAN IS: SKIVING.

IN THE KNOWLEDGE THAT THEY'LL ALL BE TOO EMBARRASSED TO QUIZ YOU ABOUT IT... GOOD, NO PROBLEMS THERE THEN.

SCRIBBLE

Alex PEATTIE + TAYLOR

AND OUR TRADING DIVISION INFORMS ME WE SHOULD BE KEEPING AN EYE ON THE SITUATION AS REGARDS ALLIED TROOPS GOING INTO IRAQ.

GOOD GRIEF. NOT AGAIN.

LOOKS LIKE IT, YES. I MUST SAY I'VE GROWN VERY CYNICAL ABOUT THIS KIND OF THING SINCE THE GULF WAR.

ME TOO.

THE WAY A TRIGGER EVENT LIKE THE INVASION OF KUWAIT WAS USED AS AN EXCUSE TO INVOLVE US IN A HUGE AND COSTLY ENTERPRISE WITH NO DISCERNABLE BENEFICIAL OUTCOME.

PUTTING NEW SCREENS ON EVERYONE'S DESK SO THEY COULD KEEP TRACK OF CNN NEWS?

YES. ALL THEY WANT TO DO IS BE ABLE TO WATCH SPORT ALL DAY WHEN IT'S QUIET...

THEY CLAIM THEY NEED SATELLITE TELLY NOW.

Alex PEATTIE + TAYLOR

HELLO. I'VE JUST MOVED INTO THE MILL COTTAGE.

BAR

ARR. WELL I SHOULD KEEP QUIET ABOUT THAT ROUND HERE IF I WAS YOU...

YOU KNOW HOW IT IS IN THESE RURAL AREAS. PEOPLE HAVE SEEN WHOLE VILLAGES BOUGHT UP BY YUPPIES FOR WEEKEND HOMES IN THE EIGHTIES...

SO NOWADAYS WHEN A TOWNIE LIKE YOU BUYS A HOUSE IN THE AREA IT'S BOUND TO CAUSE RESENTMENT FROM THE LONG-ESTABLISHED POPULACE.

THEY'RE ALL STRANDED HERE BY THE PROPERTY CRASH.

CREEP. WHY DIDN'T HE BUY _MY_ HOUSE?

...DIDN'T EVEN _LOOK_ ROUND MINE...

OURS WAS ON THE MARKET FIRST...

Alex
PEATTIE + TAYLOR

RUPERT WHAT IS THE POINT OF COMING HERE IF YOU'RE NOT GOING TO GET A TAN?

WHO'S GOING TO SEE IT CAMILLA?

AS SOON AS WE GET BACK FROM HOLIDAY I'LL BE BACK IN MY BUSINESS SUIT AND PEOPLE WILL ONLY EVER SEE MY FACE AND HANDS.

DON'T BE SILLY RUPERT. YOU DON'T GET A TAN JUST TO IMPRESS THE PEOPLE AT THE OFFICE, DO YOU?

YOU'RE RIGHT I SUPPOSE.

AND DON'T LET ME FORGET TO SEND A POSTCARD TO THE CHAPS AT THE LODGE.

NO DEAR.

PALE GLEAM

Alex PEATTIE + TAYLOR

So you're regretting getting your video phone, Sir Terence?

Yes. I'm afraid I failed to see the inherent drawbacks in it.

It just highlights the problems of being trail-blazers in modern banking — it's pointless unless a significant number of people we do business with follow our lead...

It makes me wonder how I ever allowed myself to be persuaded to spend so much of the bank's money on so foolhardy a purchase...

Of this building in Docklands?

Yes. I have to lower the blinds over this incriminating backdrop before I can use my new phone.

Alex PEATTIE + TAYLOR

You know, I'm very impressed with the way Carson has heeded my warning that he was in danger of losing his job with us.

Yes. He wasn't doing himself any favours with that attitude of his.

Well he's clearly taken to heart my advice about taking steps to avoid an ignominious end to his banking career.

In this recession one can't afford not to.

Indeed. It's good to see a person really using the chance he's been given to change his ways and display an appropriate level of enthusiasm and commitment to his work.

Yes.

...I dunno... I'm getting a bit bored and frustrated... maybe it's time for me to move on... I'm thinking of going into farming...

...instead of embarrassing himself by appearing really dedicated right up to the last minute.

He'll thank me for this when he's sacked.

Alex PEATTIE + TAYLOR

ALL MY BELONGINGS THE POLICE TOOK AWAY...MY GOLD WATCH AND CUFFLINKS... 24 CARAT GOLD RING... SOLID GOLD PEN... STERLING SILVER CIGARETTE LIGHTER... I'D JUST TAKEN ALL THAT FOR GRANTED...

WELL, THIS EXPERIENCE IS CERTAINLY TEACHING ME FOR THE FIRST TIME THE DIFFERENCE BETWEEN WHAT'S A NECESSITY AND WHAT'S NOT.

I WON'T BE THINKING IN TERMS OF LUXURIES OR STATUS SYMBOLS FROM NOW ON... NOT AFTER THE EXPERIENCE OF BEING HAULED OFF TO JAIL IN HANDCUFFS...

THE ONLY THING I'LL BE THINKING OF IS BREAKING OUT.

LOOK BLOTCHES ALL OVER BOTH WRISTS. I HAD NO IDEA I WAS ALLERGIC TO BASE METALS.

AND YOUR FACE LOOKS A BIT PUFFY NOW TOO...

Alex PEATTIE + TAYLOR

YOU'VE GOT TO WATCH OUT FOR THE OLD BILL, MATE. YOU CAN GET WELL STITCHED UP HERE.

HOW DO YOU MEAN?

YOU'VE BEEN HERE 48 HOURS... YOU'RE TIRED AND NOT THINKING STRAIGHT... SOME COPPER'S GOING TO SHOVE A BIT OF PAPER UNDER YOUR NOSE AND TELL YOU YOU WON'T GET OUT UNLESS YOU SIGN IT.

OH DON'T WORRY.

THEY INVENT THINGS TOTALLY AND THEN GET YOU TO PUT YOUR NAME TO IT... YOU HAVE TO CHECK EVERYTHING.

CLUMP... CLUMP CLUMP

SHH... LOOK OUT. HERE'S THE OLD BILL NOW...

CLICK

RATTLE

DON'T WORRY I'LL JUST STICK IT ALL ON THE OLD EXPENSE ACCOUNT.

NOW WOULD ONE OF YOU GENTLEMEN CALL ME A TAXI?

GRAB

HASTY SCRIBBLE

WELL, THAT'S THE CONFESSION SORTED.

BLIMEY.

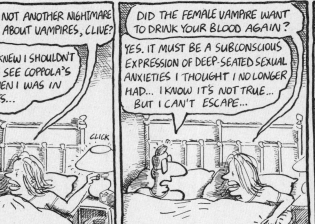

Alex
PEATTIE + TAYLOR

A DRINK, DR AND MRS VAN MASTERLEY?

A WHISKY AND A DRY SHERRY PLEASE, COUNT DRACULA.

I TELL YOU, PENELOPE, I BELIEVE OUR HOST HAS A DARK SECRET.

BUT ALEXANDER, HE SEEMS SUCH A PERFECT GENTLEMAN.

APPEARANCES CAN BE DECEPTIVE...OBSERVE IN THAT LOOKING GLASS.

OH MY GOODNESS...

HE DOESN'T HAVE A REFLECTION IN IT.

EXACTLY... AND THIS CAN ONLY MEAN ONE THING...

CURSES... DISCOVERED!.

YOU WERE RIGHT. IT IS A CLIP-ON...

NO WAY WOULD HE BE ABLE TO TIE A REAL ONE WITHOUT LOOKING IN A MIRROR.

TUG

Alex PEATTIE + TAYLOR

ALEXANDER WHY ARE WE CREEPING ROUND CASTLE DRACULA LIKE THIS?

WE HAVE TO FIND A WAY OF SLAYING THE EVIL COUNT...

YOU MEAN HE CAN BE KILLED?

MOST ASSUREDLY, PENELOPE. LEGEND TELLS OF CERTAIN TRADITIONAL VAMPIRE BANES.

THE SAFEST WAY IS TO GO FOR THE HEART.

OF COURSE! WE'RE GOING TO NEED TO PREPARE A LARGE STAKE...

EXCELLENT SIRLOIN THIS...

THE CHOLESTEROL'S BOUND TO GET HIM IN THE END AS THERE'S NO WAY HE CAN TAKE THESE GARLIC PILLS...

POP

GARLIC PILLS

Alex
PEATTIE + TAYLOR

THE ECHO

YOU'RE GOING TO LIVE AS A TRAMP FOR A FEW DAYS TO DO A STORY ABOUT THE HOMELESS AT CHRISTMAS?

FEATURES DESK

THE ECHO

I AM, YES.

YOU'RE NOT REALLY GOING TO SLEEP OUT IN THE OPEN IN THIS WEATHER, GREG?

WITH AN ASSIGNMENT LIKE THIS, I'LL HAVE TO, JULES.

IT'S A QUESTION OF MY PROFESSIONALISM AS A JOURNALIST. ACTUALLY SLEEPING ROUGH MYSELF IS A MATTER OF PRINCIPLE TO ME.

I SUPPOSE SO...

I GUESS IT'S THE ONLY WAY YOU CAN FIDDLE YOUR EXPENSES.

THAT'S RIGHT... I CAN STILL CLAIM FOR A HOSTEL YOU SEE.

Alex PEATTIE + TAYLOR

I KNOW IT'S A FASHIONABLE OPTION THESE DAYS TO LUNCH CLIENTS IN PUBS WITH STRIPPERS BUT I HADN'T EXPECTED CLIVE TO BRING US HERE...

SOMEHOW HE DOESN'T SEEM THE TYPE TO RELISH AN OCCASION WHERE YOUNG LADIES TAKE THEIR CLOTHES OFF FOR THE GRATIFICATION OF THE MALE CLIENTELE...

ON THE CONTRARY...

MANY OF THESE TIMID INHIBITED MEN REVEL IN THE UNACCUSTOMED SENSE OF POWER IT GIVES THEM OVER THE WOMAN WHO IS PRESENTED IN FRONT OF THEM EXPOSED AND SEEMINGLY AVAILABLE...

THE BARMAID YOU MEAN?

ER...

QUITE. THIS IS THE ONLY TIME CLIVE CAN MANAGE TO GET SERVED.

Alex PEATTIE + TAYLOR

CAREFUL, PENNY. DON'T SIT IN YOU-KNOW-WHO'S CHAIR.

NO. DON'T SIT THERE.

OH DEAR. ARE WE HAVING SUPPER WITH CHRISTOPHER'S IMAGINARY COMPANION AGAIN?

SHH...YES WE ARE, PENNY. AND THESE LITTLE MAKE-BELIEVE GAMES ARE AN IMPORTANT STAGE IN THE PROCESS OF CHRISTOPHER'S DEVELOPMENT TO BECOMING A FULLY SOCIALISED INDIVIDUAL.

IT'S SO SILLY.

CHILD PSYCHOLOGY

LOOK, APPARENTLY INVENTING A NON-EXISTENT PERSON TO HAVE AS A MEALTIME COMPANION ETC WILL HELP HIM TO MAKE THE TRANSITION TO BEING CONFIDENT ABOUT THE SAME SITUATION IN REAL LIFE.

YES YES... I KNOW...

INVENTING NON-EXISTENT MEALTIME COMPANIONS FOR HIS CLIENT HOSPITALITY EXPENSES CLAIMS...

EXACTLY. NOW WHAT HAS HE BEEN TALKING TO YOU ABOUT, CHRISTOPHER?

ER... A BOND ISSUE?

Alex PEATTIE + TAYLOR

HOW'S IT BEEN, SPENDING THE WEEK AT OUR COUNTRY COTTAGE?

WELL, I SEEM TO HAVE BEEN TALKING TO SO MANY PEOPLE YOU'RE ON FIRST NAME TERMS WITH...

AH, YES... THAT'S BECAUSE I'VE BEEN MAKING STRENUOUS EFFORTS TO SUGGEST THAT I NOW LIVE PERMANENTLY HERE IN THE VILLAGE. I DON'T LIKE TO BE THOUGHT OF AS A WEEKENDER...

THE TROUBLE IS, THE SORT OF COMMUNICATION ONE HAS WITH THESE PEOPLE IS SO SUPERFICIAL. ALL ONE REALLY KNOWS ABOUT THEM IS THEIR FIRST NAME AND A VAGUE IDEA AS TO WHAT THEIR JOB MIGHT BE...

HEADHUNTERS HAVE TO BE CAUTIOUS, PENNY. THAT'S WHY THEY INSTINCTIVELY PHONE MY HOME NUMBER...

WELL, TIM, MICHAEL, PAUL AND DONALD ALL WANT YOU TO CALL THEM BACK.

Alex PEATTIE + TAYLOR

THANKS SO MUCH FOR STOPPING. YOU CAN SEE MY PREDICAMENT. MY REAR WHEELS ARE STUCK FAST IN THE MUD...

MY CAR'S NOT REALLY MADE FOR THIS SORT OF TERRAIN...

YES. I COULD SEE IMMEDIATELY THAT IT WAS A SITUATION WHERE IT WOULD BE HANDY TO HAVE MY RANGE ROVER...

YOU SEE MY VEHICLE IS INTENDED TO BE DRIVEN OFF THE ROAD... RIGHT, NOW... DO YOU WANT TO TRY REVVING UP YOUR CAR?

OKAY...

HMM... A MOST IMPRESSIVE COATING, AND MUCH QUICKER THAN APPLYING THE MUD BY HAND. THANKYOU.

ER... ACTUALLY I WAS RATHER HOPING YOU WERE GOING TO TOW ME OUT...

SPLAT SPLAT

REV REV

WHIRR

Alex — PEATTIE + TAYLOR

Panel 1: THAT GENTLEMAN JUST FAINTED. / DON'T WORRY, EVERYONE. I'M LOOKING AFTER HIM.

Panel 2: HE'D BEEN TO SEE ME FOR A CONSULTATION. HE WAS JUST LEAVING WHEN HE COLLAPSED...

Panel 3: AH... RUPERT. BACK WITH US? HOW ARE YOU FEELING? / JONATHAN... OH LOOK I'M FINE HONESTLY...

Panel 4: ARE YOU SURE YOU DON'T WANT ME TO CALL AN AMBULANCE FOR YOU? / NO NO... REALLY...

Panel 5: I'LL GET A PASSER-BY TO DO IT. IT'LL BE MUCH CHEAPER... / OKAY. SO I'LL JUST BILL YOU FOR THE EXTRA TWO MINUTES THEN... / SOLICITORS AT LAW

Alex — PEATTIE + TAYLOR

Panel 1: IT UPSETS ME WHEN THE PAPERS SUGGEST THAT THE COURT WOULD TREAT US MORE HARSHLY IF WE WERE COMMON CRIMINALS RATHER THAN WHITE COLLAR BANKERS... / COURT No 3 ← / NEWS CITY FRAUD MEN IN THE DOCK / BROMEX TRIAL STARTS TODAY

Panel 2: THE IMPLICATION THAT SUCH TRIALS WORK ON THE BASIS OF "ONE LAW FOR THE RICH, ONE LAW FOR THE POOR"—IT'S MOST OFFENSIVE. / YES, IT SHOWS A BASIC MISCONCEPTION ABOUT WHAT'S INVOLVED IN A CASE LIKE OURS. / COURT No 3 ←

Panel 3: I MEAN, WHAT WE'RE DEBATING IS THE ALLEGED NATURE OF COMPLEX ABSTRACT TRANSFERS OF MILLIONS OF POUNDS SUPPOSEDLY TO RAMP THE THEORETICAL VALUE OF A PUBLIC COMPANY. / COURT No 3 ←

Panel 4: YOU WOULDN'T FIND ANYONE POOR BEING CHARGED WITH OFFENCES LIKE THAT. / QUITE. THEY COULDN'T AFFORD TO COMMIT THEM. / COURT No 3 ←

Alex
PEATTIE + TAYLOR

COURT No 2

MORNING. — SHHH.

WAS IT REALLY NECESSARY TO SNUB THAT POOR JURY MEMBER, CRISPIN?

IT'S IN EVERYONE'S BEST INTEREST IF ONE ADHERES STRICTLY TO THE COURT RULES ABOUT JURY MEMBERS NOT CONVERSING WITH LAWYERS ON THE CASE

AS A LAY PERSON ONE MIGHT NOT EXPECT HIM TO APPRECIATE THE CONSEQUENCES OF CASUAL SOCIAL EXCHANGES BUT AS A LEGAL PROFESSIONAL I AM OBLIGED TO KEEP A WATCH FOR THESE THINGS.

A STOP WATCH?

YES. 800 GUINEAS AN HOUR, REMEMBER? I DOUBT HE COULD AFFORD IT.

Alex
PEATTIE + TAYLOR

SIR REGINALD, I NOTE YOU TAKE THE SAME MORNING TRAIN AS THE ACCUSED. THE 7.26 TO WATERLOO.

IN VIEW OF YOUR SUBSEQUENT SHARE-DEALINGS BEFORE THE BROMEX TAKEOVER WAS ANNOUNCED, IS IT NOT CONCEIVABLE THAT MR STERLING MIGHT HAVE GIVEN YOU A TIP?

GIVEN ME A TIP?

M'LUD, MR STERLING IS A GENTLEMAN AND AN ESTEEMED MEMBER OF THE CITY ESTABLISHMENT. NOW HE IS ACCUSED OF HAVING BROKEN THE MOST HALLOWED PRINCIPLES OF THAT AUGUST INSTITUTION...

EXCHANGE WORDS WITH ANOTHER OCCUPANT OF ONE'S FIRST CLASS CARRIAGE? NEVER!

Alex — PEATTIE + TAYLOR

Panel 1: DARLING, ABOUT YOU CRYING IN COURT. YOU MUST REALISE THERE'S NO POINT WORRYING ABOUT ME. I'M BASICALLY QUITE A FORTUNATE MAN.
YES...
COURT NO 3 ←

Panel 2: IF YOU'RE GOING TO GET UPSET YOU SHOULD THINK OF ALL THE PEOPLE IN THE WORLD WHO HAVE REAL PROBLEMS LIKE DISEASE AND HUNGER AND POVERTY. NOT SOMEONE LIKE ME.
ALL RIGHT RUPERT.

Panel 3: AND WHEN YOU TAKE THE STAND REMEMBER IF THE WORST COMES TO THE WORST YOU CAN ALWAYS JUST COVER YOUR FACE WITH YOUR HANDS LIKE THIS FOR A FEW MOMENTS...

Panel 4: ...AND TUG OUT A HAIR FROM YOUR NOSTRIL. THAT USUALLY BRINGS A TEAR TO THE EYE.
OKAY.
GOOD GIRL.

Alex — PEATTIE + TAYLOR

Panel 1: WELL, WE HAVE AMPLE EVIDENCE THAT YOU HAD NUMEROUS CONTACTS WITH MR STERLING OF WHOM YOU NOW CLAIM TO HAVE NO MEMORY...
NO MEMORY AT ALL I'M AFRAID.

Panel 2: THIS TOTAL AMNESIA SEEMS VERY CONVENIENT, MR GRAHAM. YOU ARE, ARE YOU NOT, ATTEMPTING TO PROTECT YOUR PROFESSIONAL REPUTATION?
SORRY. MY MIND'S A BLANK ON THIS ONE

Panel 3: LOOK, IT HAS BEEN ESTABLISHED THAT YOU SAW A PERSON WHO CAME TO THE BANK WHERE YOU WORK ON THE DAY IN QUESTION...

Panel 4: NOW I'M GOING TO ASK YOU AGAIN: DO YOU RECOGNISE THAT MAN IN THIS COURT?

Panel 5: NOT WITHOUT HIS SECURITY PASS I DON'T. NO.
GRRR
WHAT A FIBBER! BANK DOORMEN. THEY'RE ALL THE SAME...

Alex PEATTIE + TAYLOR

MIGHT I REFER YOU TO THE LISTING OF "PARTEX N.V."..."N.V." BEING THE ACRONYM FOR COMPANIES REGISTERED ANONYMOUSLY IN THE DUTCH ANTILLES.

WHAT ABOUT IT?

NOW, YOU HAVE MAINTAINED THAT IT IS PERFECTLY NORMAL, STRAIGHTFORWARD AND ABOVE-BOARD PRACTICE TO SET UP A HOLDING COMPANY LIKE THIS FOR MULTI-MILLION POUND SHARE DEALINGS AND PAYMENTS OF HUGE CONSULTANCY FEES...

BUT DO YOU KNOW WHAT KEEPS GOING THROUGH MY HEAD?

NO. WHAT?

"N.V."!... N.V., N.V., N.V.!

AHAH SO YOU ADMIT IT THEN? YOU'RE ABSOLUTELY GREEN WITH IT! ...MY LORD, I SUBMIT THE PROSECUTION'S CASE IS BASED ON SHEER SPITE.

Alex PEATTIE + TAYLOR

SO WHAT YOU ARE SAYING IS THAT THE SITUATION YOU FIND YOURSELF IN IS NOT ONE FOR WHICH YOU FEEL YOU ARE PRIMARILY RESPONSIBLE?

THAT'S RIGHT.

I'VE SAT HERE WATCHING EVIDENCE MOUNT UP AS A CASE BUILDS MOMENTUM WHICH NOW SEEMS ALMOST CERTAIN TO CONVICT ME AND I BELIEVE THE TIME HAS COME TO BREAK MY SILENCE.

I MADE A SIMPLE ERROR OF PLACING MY TRUST IN THE PROFESSIONAL ADVICE OF OTHERS WHO MISLED ME AND I WISH TO MAKE IT QUITE CLEAR WHO SHOULD BE TAKING THE BLAME.

RIGHT. WHO?

MY BLOODY DEFENCE LAWYER. YOU'RE SACKED CRISPIN. YOU'RE OBVIOUSLY TOTALLY INCOMPETENT.

OH. FAIR ENOUGH...

Alex PEATTIE + TAYLOR

THE EUROPEAN BANK OF RECONSTRUCTION AND DEVELOPMENT HAS HAD SOME BAD PUBLICITY RECENTLY, PIERRE.

JUST BECAUSE WE PUT EXPENSIVE MARBLE IN OUR FOYER? PAH!

E.B.R.D.

YOU KNOW, CLIVE, WE FRENCH BANKERS UNDERSTAND THE GREAT AND NOBLE TASK WE FACE - TO HELP TO REBUILD AN EASTERN EUROPE THAT HAS BEEN ECONOMICALLY CUT OFF FOR 50 YEARS.

GREAT CHANGES HAVE HAPPENED, CLIVE. THE CURTAIN HAS BEEN TORN DOWN, THE WALL HAS BEEN DEMOLISHED...

YES INDEED.

IN FACT YOU'RE HAVING YOUR WHOLE OFFICE EXTENSIVELY REFITTED..

HOW DID THEY EXPECT ME TO WORK WITH THAT AWFUL PETIT BOURGEOIS DECOR?

Alex PEATTIE + TAYLOR

SO THIS IS YOUR COMPOSTER?

YES. NOW WE'VE HAD IT FOR A YEAR WE'RE JUST STARTING TO SEE THE BENEFITS...

IT'S NOT JUST FOR GARDEN CUTTINGS AND VEGETABLE PEEL...GUESTS HERE ARE ALWAYS TAKEN ABACK WHEN I REVEAL THE EXTENT OF ITEMS WE NO LONGER PUT IN THE DUSTBIN...

TEA BAGS, NEWSPAPERS, RAGS, OLD CLOTHES... ANYTHING ORGANIC WILL ROT DOWN WITH TIME.. SEE FOR YOURSELF.

EEK!

AH YES. THESE HOLEY OLD SOCKS YOU THREW AWAY WHEN YOU STAYED LAST YEAR...STILL INTACT... AS I SUSPECTED: POLYESTER.

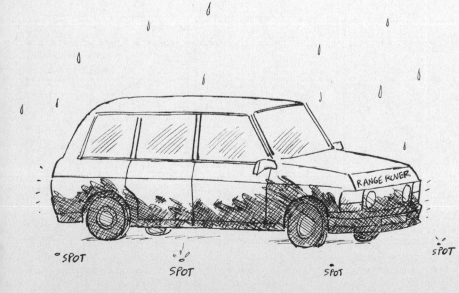

Alex PEATTIE + TAYLOR

IT'S A GREAT FEELING BEING ABLE TO JOG PAST OUR WORK COLLEAGUES TRAPPED IMMOBILE IN THE AGGRAVATED RUSH HOUR TRAFFIC...

IT CERTAINLY IS...

THOSE OF US IN TRAINING FOR THE LONDON MARATHON AREN'T BOTHERED BY TODAY'S ALL OUT TRANSPORT STRIKE. WE CAN JUST RUN TO WORK.

HONK?

TAXI

QUITE.

FRANKLY THIS SHOULD PROVE INVALUABLE IN HELPING US OVERCOME THAT ARDUOUS AND GRUELLING CHALLENGE WE HAVE TAKEN UPON OURSELVES...

IT'S THE IDEAL OPPORTUNITY...

A CAPTIVE AUDIENCE WHO CAN'T CLAIM TO BE TOO BUSY TO SPONSOR US...

OH, ALEX...HI....

TAP TAP TAP

SPONSORSHIP FORM

Alex PEATTIE + TAYLOR

READ MY LETTER BACK SO FAR, PLEASE, NORRIS.

"AS A BUSINESSMAN IN PRISON I AM NOW AWARE OF WHAT A TIGHTROPE ONE TREADS WITH REGARD TO BRITISH FINANCIAL REGULATIONS."

"...IN MY VIEW WELL PUBLICISED GUIDELINES ARE NEEDED BY THE BUSINESS COMMUNITY IF COSTLY AND PUNITIVE COURT CASES ARE TO BE AVOIDED..."

"IT IS PARAMOUNT FOR INDIVIDUALS WHO DON'T WANT TO END UP IN PRISON, TO ENSURE THAT WHAT THEY DO IS LEGIT."

ER... SHOULD BE A SPACE THERE, NORRIS.

OH YES... WHOOPS.

SO IT'S: "ENSURE THAT WHAT THEY DO IS LEG IT"...

THANKYOU. YES...

CONTINUING: "ANYWAY, I WISH ID SEEN THE LIGHT A BIT EARLIER MYSELF. NICE ONE, ASIL. YOURS AYE, RUPERT."

THEN SEND IT TO CYPRUS FIRST CLASS.